Developing Num

USING AND APPLYING MATHS

INVESTIGATIONS FOR THE DAILY MATHS LESSON

year 3

Hilary Koll and Steve Mills

A & C BLACK

Mathematical skills and processes

Page	Activity title	Predict	Visualise	Look for pattern	Record	Reason	Make decisions	Estimate	Explain	Be systematic	Co-operate	Compare	Test ideas	Trial and improvement	Ask own questions	Generalise	Check
	Numbers and the number system																
14	Wild about animals	●	○	○		○						○	●			○	
15	Star trekking		○		○	○	○			○			●	●			
16	Half-time scores	○		●		○		●		○	○	○				○	
17	Digit riddles	○		●						●			○				○
18	On the buses			○		○	●			●							○
19	A space oddity	●		○		○				○			○			●	●
	Calculations																
20	Total teaser: 1			○		○				●			○				○
21	Total teaser: 2			●		○				●	○						
22	Terrific tiles	○	○	○		●	●						○				
23	Lily pads			●		○			○			●				○	○
24	Piles of coins			●	○	○		○									
25	Eggs in nests			○	○			○	●		●						
26–27	'Gazinta' puzzles: 1 and 2		○	○	○	●		○		○			○				○
28–29	Wheel meet again: 1 and 2			●	○					○			○		●		
	Solving problems																
30	Morse code: 1			○						●							
31	Morse code: 2			●		○							○				
32	Permutation puzzles		○	○	○			○		●		○				○	
33	Hit the right note									●		○	○			○	
34	Counter intelligence		●			○	●				●	○	○				
35	Trumpet tunes			○						●		○				○	
36–37	Magic keys: 1 and 2	●		●			○					○	○				
	Handling data																
38	Telephone buttons				●								○	●	○	○	
39	Dotty domino patterns	○		●						○	●						
	Measures, shape and space																
40	Wands	○			○			●			●		○				○
41	Time for a game	○			○			●			●		○				○
42	Hungry hamster		○		●	○						○					
43	Pampered pets		○	○		●						○			●		○
44–45	Helicopter pads: 1 and 2			●		○			○	○						○	
46	3-D puzzles	○	●									○	○				
47	Letter lines	●	●							○			●				
48	Leap and swap		○		○	●				○			●				

● Key processes identified on the activity sheet   ○ Additional processes involved in the activity

Contents

Handling data

Measures, shape and space

Published 2005 by A & C Black Publishers Limited
37 Soho Square, London W1D 3QZ
www.acblack.com

ISBN-10: 0-7136-7138-6
ISBN-13: 978-0-7136-7138-4

Copyright text © Hilary Koll and Steve Mills, 2005
Copyright illustrations © Pat Murray, 2005
Copyright cover illustration © Charlotte Hard, 2005
Editors: Lynne Williamson and Marie Lister
Designer: Heather Billin

The authors and publishers would like to thank Jane McNeill and Catherine Yemm for their advice in producing this series of books.

A CIP catalogue record for this book is available from the British Library.

Printed and bound in Great Britain by Cromwell Press Ltd, Trowbridge, Wiltshire.

A & C Black uses paper produced with elemental chlorine-free pulp, harvested from managed sustainable forests.

Introduction

Developing Numeracy: Using and Applying Maths is a series of seven photocopiable activity books designed to be used during the daily maths lesson. The books focus on using and applying mathematics, as referred to in the National Numeracy Strategy *Framework for teaching mathematics*. The activities are intended to be used in the time allocated to pupil activities during the main part of the lesson. They are designed to develop and reinforce the skills and processes that are vital to help children use and apply their maths.

Using and applying mathematics

There are several different components which make up the **content** of maths and form the bulk of any maths curriculum:

- **mathematical facts**, for example, a triangle has three sides;
- **mathematical skills**, such as counting;
- **mathematical concepts**, like place value.

For maths teaching to be successful, it is vital that children can *use* this mathematical content beyond their classroom, either in real-life situations or as a basis for further understanding. However, in order to do so, they require extra abilities over and above the mathematical content they have learned. These extra abilities are often referred to as the **processes** of mathematical activity. It is these processes which make mathematical content usable.

As an example, consider this question:
How many triangles are there in this shape?

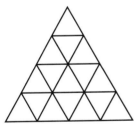

The mathematical content required is only:
- the **fact** that a triangle has three sides;
- the **skill** of counting.

As such, it could be expected that very young children could solve this problem. The fact that they cannot suggests that other abilities are involved. These are the processes, and for this question they include:
- visualising the different-sized triangles;
- being systematic in counting all the triangles of different sizes;
- looking for patterns in the numbers of triangles;
- trial and improvement;
- recording.

Unless children can apply these processes in this situation, then however good their counting skills and knowledge of triangles may be, they will fail.

The 'solving problems' strand of the *Framework for teaching mathematics* emphasises the importance of using and applying mathematics. This series of books is intended to make explicit the skills and processes involved in learning how to put maths knowledge to use.

Using and Applying Maths Year 3 supports the development of the using and applying processes by providing opportunities to introduce and practise them through a series of activities. On the whole these activities are designed for children to work on independently, although this is not always possible and occasionally some children may need support.

Pre-school children are naturally inquisitive about the world around them. They love to explore and experiment, and to make marks and record things on paper in their own idiosyncratic ways. Unfortunately, once at school the focus is often placed firmly on the maths content alone and children can be led to believe that maths is not a subject of exploration, but rather one of simply learning the 'right way to do things'. As a result, when older children are asked to explore and investigate maths they are often at a loss if their maths teaching to date has not encouraged and built upon their natural instincts.

Year 3 helps children to develop the following processes:

- predicting
- visualising
- looking for pattern
- recording
- reasoning
- making decisions
- estimating
- explaining
- being systematic
- co-operating
- comparing
- testing ideas
- trial and improvement
- asking own questions
- generalising
- checking

When using these activities, the focus need not be on the actual mathematical content. Instead, the teacher's demonstrations, discussions and questioning should emphasise the processes the children are using. A summary of the skills and processes covered by each activity is shown on page 2. When appropriate, invite the children to explain their thinking to others. Research has shown that children develop processes most successfully when the teacher encourages them to act as experts rather than novices, allowing them to work autonomously and encouraging a range of approaches to any problem rather than constraining discussion to produce an overall class plan. The children should evaluate their own plans against other plans in the posing, planning and monitoring phases of the lessons.

Extension

Many of the activity sheets end with a challenge (**Now try this!**) which reinforces and extends the children's learning, and provides the teacher with an opportunity for assessment. On occasion, it may be helpful to read the instructions

with the children before they begin the activity. For some of the challenges the children will need to record their answers on a separate piece of paper.

Organisation

Very little equipment is needed, but it will be useful to have the following resources available: coloured pencils, counters, scissors, coins, squared paper, number lines and number tracks.

To help teachers select appropriate learning experiences for the children, the activities are grouped into sections within the book. However, the activities are not expected to be used in this order unless stated otherwise. The sheets are intended to support, rather than direct, the teacher's planning.

Some activities can be made easier or more challenging by masking or substituting numbers. You may wish to re-use pages by copying them onto card and laminating them.

Teachers' notes

Brief notes are provided at the foot of each page giving ideas and suggestions for maximising the effectiveness of the activity sheets. These can be masked before copying.

Solutions and further explanations of the activities can be found on pages 7–13, together with examples of questions that you can ask.

Whole class warm-up activities

The following activities provide some practical ideas which can be used to introduce the main teaching part of the lesson.

Looking for pattern, testing ideas and explaining

On the board, draw a 4×4 grid with a number in each square, for example:

36	4	24	2
8	16	3	15
20	7	12	19
40	25	6	10

Ask the children to create number statements using the numbers in the grid, for example:

$4 \times 10 = 40$, $25 - 15 = 10$, $16 + 4 = 20$, $20 \div 2 = 10$

(It can be useful to draw a blank template on card and laminate it. New numbers can then be written in with a dry-wipe marker pen whenever required.)

Estimating

Show the children a metre stick. Ask them to estimate (in metres): the distance across the classroom; the height from floor to ceiling; the length of a window. Write the estimates on the board. Choose a smaller unit of measure, such as a ruler or pencil, and ask further questions.

Reasoning

Pick a shape from a bag of flat shapes, but do not show it to the children. The children can ask you three questions, to which you answer *Yes* or *No* (for example, *Does it have five corners?*).

For a more challenging version, use 3-D shapes.

Being systematic

Write the number 15 on the board. Ask the children to suggest ways of adding three odd numbers to make 15: for example, $1 + 5 + 9$, $11 + 3 + 1$. List correct suggestions on the board and prompt the children to look for more: *How many threes have we written? How many nines? Are we missing any?* Begin to organise the list so that all the number statements beginning with '1' come together (i.e. $1 + 3 + 11$, $1 + 5 + 9$...). The class should decide together whether a digit can be used more than once (for example, $3 + 3 + 9$).

Notes on the activities

Numbers and the number system

Wild about animals (page 14)

☆ *Processes: predict, test ideas, look for pattern, visualise, reason, compare, generalise*

This activity focuses on predicting. It encourages the children to see the benefits of looking for patterns in the numbers to assist them with their predictions.

Answers are as follows:

1. elephant   elephant   elephant
   tiger   giraffe   tiger

2. tiger   6th, 12th, 18th, 24th, 30th, 36th, 42nd, 48th, 54th, 60th

   monkey   5th, 11th, 17th, 23rd, 29th, 35th, 41st, 47th, 53rd, 59th

   elephant   1st, 4th, 7th, 10th, 13th, 16th, 19th, 22nd, 25th, 28th

   lion   3rd, 9th, 15th, 21st, 27th, 33rd, 39th, 45th, 51st, 57th

   giraffe   2nd, 8th, 14th, 20th, 26th, 32nd, 38th, 44th, 50th, 56th

3. tiger   monkey   elephant

Patterns that the children might notice include:

- the tiger numbers are all multiples of 6
- the monkey numbers are one less than the tiger numbers
- the elephant numbers go up in threes
- the lion numbers are the odd multiples of 3 and are three less than the tiger numbers
- the giraffe numbers are one less than the lion numbers.

Suggested questions:

- How can you be sure?
- What made you predict that? How could you check?
- What if we had five animals?

Star trekking (page 15)

☆ *Processes: test ideas, trial and improvement, make decisions, reason, record, be systematic, visualise*

This puzzle has a number of different routes that involve fewer than five multiples of 5. Some of these routes begin with two multiples of 5, and the children may be put off by having to give up two cubes immediately – but they will find the routes better in the long run. Such activities encourage the children to think tactically, so that rather than following routes blindly they, perhaps, examine routes and work backwards from the finish. Ask the children to think about what they have learned from each route they try. They could mark numbers with a tick or a cross for quicker work. For further extension work, they could make their own puzzle of this type, or try mazes where numbers are multiples of other numbers.

Suggested questions/prompts:

- Which ways have you tried? Make a record of your routes. What have you learned from these routes?
- What strategies could you use? Could you try working backwards from the finish?

Half-time scores (page 16)

☆ *Processes: look for pattern, explain, reason, be systematic, predict, compare, co-operate, ask own questions*

Answers are as follows:

1. (a) 0 : 0
        0 : 0, 1 : 0
        0 : 0, 1 : 0, 2 : 0
        0 : 0, 1 : 0, 2 : 0, 3 : 0
        0 : 0, 1 : 0, 2 : 0, 3 : 0, 4 : 0
        0 : 0, 1 : 0, 2 : 0, 3 : 0, 4 : 0, 5 : 0

   (b) 10
   (The pattern for the number of possible half-time scores is one more than the number of goals scored.)

2. (a) 0 : 0, 1 : 0, 0 : 1, 1 : 1
        0 : 0, 1 : 0, 0 : 1, 1 : 1, 2 : 0, 0 : 2, 2 : 1, 1 : 2, 2 : 2
        0 : 0, 1 : 0, 0 : 1, 1 : 1, 2 : 0, 0 : 2, 2 : 1, 1 : 2, 2 : 2, 3 : 0, 0 : 3, 3 : 1, 1 : 3, 3 : 2, 2 : 3, 3 : 3

The pattern in the number of possible half-time scores is: 1 way for 0 : 0, 4 ways for 1 : 1, 9 ways for 2 : 2, 16 ways for 3 : 3. Whilst you would not necessarily choose to discuss this with children of this age, this forms a pattern of square numbers, thus there would be 25 possible half-time scores for a 4 : 4 draw.

For children of this age, it is sufficient to provide them with opportunities to find all the possible solutions and to check that they have found the complete set.

Suggested questions:

- What have you discovered?
- How can you be sure that you have found all the solutions?
- How could you check?

Digit riddles (page 17)

☆ *Processes: look for pattern, be systematic, predict, test ideas, check*

There are nine solutions between 0 and 100: 11, 22, 33, 44, 55, 66, 77, 88 and 99. The number 100 also fits the description and so could be the secret number. It is the solutions between 100 and 200 that the children are most likely to miss; there are 27 solutions between 100 and 200. When shown in a grid, the patterns can be seen more easily (see diagram overleaf).

101	102	103	104	105	106	107	108	109	110
111	112	113	114	115	116	117	118	119	120
121	122	123	124	125	126	127	128	129	130
131	132	133	134	135	136	137	138	139	140
141	142	143	144	145	146	147	148	149	150
151	152	153	154	155	156	157	158	159	160
161	162	163	164	165	166	167	168	169	170
171	172	173	174	175	176	177	178	179	180
181	182	183	184	185	186	187	188	189	190
191	192	193	194	195	196	197	198	199	200

(Circled numbers: 101, 110, 111, 112, 113, 114, 115, 116, 117, 118, 119, 121, 122, 131, 133, 141, 144, 151, 155, 161, 166, 171, 177, 181, 188, 191, 199)

Suggested questions:

- What patterns have you noticed?
- How many numbers like this do you think there might be between 200 and 300?
- Which are odd numbers?

On the buses (page 18)

☆ Processes: be systematic, make decisions, look for pattern, reason, check

If the children choose to include the original six numbers in their list, there are 26 possibilities; if not, there are 20.

They can be ordered as follows:
Less than 100:   5, 7, 30, 40, 35, 37, 45, 47
Greater than 100:   200, 600, 205, 207, 605, 607, 230, 240, 630, 640, 235, 237, 245, 247, 635, 637, 645, 647

When 1000 is included, there are an additional 27 possible numbers (for example, 1000, 1005, 1007…), making the total number 53.

Suggested questions:

- Do you think you have found them all?
- How could you order your numbers to check?
- What other questions could you ask about your answers? Which is your largest/smallest number?

A space oddity (page 19)

☆ Processes: generalise, predict, check, look for pattern, explain, reason, test ideas

This activity encourages the children to explore the number of odd numbers between consecutive multiples of 10 and to make generalisations about whether the same number would occur between other consecutive multiples of 10. Stress the importance of checking predictions.

There are five odd numbers in each decade, thus there are 50 odd numbers between 0 and 100, and 500 between 0 and 1000.

Suggested questions:

- What have you noticed about odd numbers?
- Do you think this is always the case?
- What helped you to make this prediction?
- Can you explain what you have discovered?

Calculations

Total teaser: 1 (page 20)

☆ Processes: be systematic, look for pattern, reason, trial and improvement, check

Each total from 1 to 30 can be made using the numbers 1, 2, 4, 8 and 16. There is only one way of making each total (when the numbers can be used only once).

1	1	16	16
2	2	17	1 + 16
3	1 + 2	18	2 + 16
4	4	19	1 + 2 + 16
5	1 + 4	20	4 + 16
6	2 + 4	21	1 + 4 + 16
7	1 + 2 + 4	22	2 + 4 + 16
8	8	23	1 + 2 + 4 + 16
9	1 + 8	24	8 + 16
10	2 + 8	25	1 + 8 + 16
11	1 + 2 + 8	26	2 + 8 + 16
12	4 + 8	27	1 + 2 + 8 + 16
13	1 + 4 + 8	28	4 + 8 + 16
14	2 + 4 + 8	29	1 + 4 + 8 + 16
15	1 + 2 + 4 + 8	30	2 + 4 + 8 + 16

Encourage the children to describe any patterns they notice in the numbers and how they found them.

For the extension activity, all numbers up to 63 can be made in the same way.

Suggested questions:

- What patterns did you notice in the numbers?
- What is the highest possible total?

Total teaser: 2 (page 21)

☆ Processes: be systematic, look for pattern, reason, co-operate

The completed cards should be:

1	3	5
7	9	11
13	15	17
19	21	23
25	27	29

2	3	6
7	10	11
14	15	18
19	22	23
26	27	30

4	5	6
7	12	13
14	15	20
21	22	23
28	29	30

8	9	10
11	12	13
14	15	24
25	26	27
28	29	30

16	17	18
19	20	21
22	23	24
25	26	27
28	29	30

For the extension activity, explain how to perform the following magic trick. The 'magician' shuffles the cards and places them face up on the table. Another child chooses a number between 1 and 30 and keeps it secret. He or she then finds all the cards with that number on and hands them to the magician. The magician finds out the secret number by adding up the bold corner numbers on all the cards selected.

Terrific tiles (page 22)

☆ *Processes: make decisions, reason, predict, visualise, look for pattern, trial and improvement*

This activity combines several aspects of maths (including symmetry, finding totals, multiplication and money notation) and provides the children with opportunities to explore, look for patterns and make generalisations. The children first create different symmetrical patterns and work out the cost. They may then begin to notice patterns in the totals and designs: for example, excluding the central tile, there will be an even number of tiles of each type. This may lead them to realise that, excluding the central tile, the total price will be even and therefore if the 10p or 12p tile is in the centre the total price will be even. If the central tile is 15p then the total will be odd.

Designs could be made into displays to encourage further discussion and investigation.

Example solutions for the extension activity are:

95p

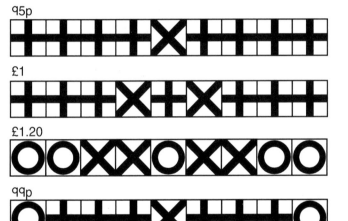

£1

£1.20

99p

£1.01 and 93p are not possible.

Suggested questions/prompts:
- Look at where the different types of tile are in this symmetrical design. What do you notice?
- Which totals between £1 and £1.50 is it possible to make?
- If you use all three types of tile, what is the most/least expensive design you can make?

Lily pads (page 23)

☆ *Processes: look for pattern, compare, check, explain, reason, ask own questions*

Encourage the children to discuss the patterns created with a partner and to suggest reasons for the patterns.

Differences	Number of lines
30	6
40	5
50	4
60	3
70	2
80	1

For the extension activity, the children can be encouraged to ask their own questions and to choose which other totals or differences to explore. They could even extend the investigation by exploring other numbers of lily pads or placing them in different arrangements.

Suggested questions:
- How would you describe the pattern you have made?
- How is it different from this pattern?
- How many lines did you draw on this diagram?
- Can you see a pattern in the numbers of lines for each difference?
- What other ways could you explore these ideas?

Piles of coins (page 24)

☆ *Processes: look for pattern, record, reason, explain*

The children should find that for each of the examples given, the coins fall into a pattern of 4 8 → 8 4 → 4 8 → 8 4..., where the smaller pile (4) is doubled (8) leaving 4 on the other pile. This occurs in most cases where 12 coins are used. There are exceptions, such as piles of 9 and 3 which end with 6 and 6.

There are many other patterns that occur for different numbers of coins. For example, piles of 4 and 6 result in a repeating pattern of moves: 4 6 → 8 2 → 6 4 → 2 8 → 4 6 → 8 2 → 6 4 → 2 8...

The children should be encouraged to discuss how best to record the outcomes, whether by using small drawings or notation of some kind, for example:

4	6
8	2
6	4
2	8

Suggested questions:
- What did you notice?
- Is it the same for these starting piles?
- How could we record this?

Eggs in nests (page 25)

☆ *Processes: be systematic, compare, look for pattern, record, explain*

Encourage the children to collaborate by comparing their solutions with a partner first and then as a whole class. Compile a list of solutions on the board and ask questions about them, such as, 'How many solutions involve a nest with two eggs?' Show that looking for pattern can help them to check their solutions.

Here are the ten solutions:

			Total
0	0	0	0
0	0	1	1
0	0	2	2
0	1	1	2
0	1	2	3
1	1	1	3
0	2	2	4
1	1	2	4
1	2	2	5
2	2	2	6

For the extension activity, there are 20 solutions:

			total
0	0	0	**0**
0	0	1	**1**
0	0	2	**2**
0	1	1	**2**
0	0	3	**3**
0	1	2	**3**
1	1	1	**3**
0	1	3	**4**
0	2	2	**4**
1	1	2	**4**
0	2	3	**5**
1	1	3	**5**
1	2	2	**5**
0	3	3	**6**
1	2	3	**6**
2	2	2	**6**
1	3	3	**7**
2	2	3	**7**
2	3	3	**8**
3	3	3	**9**

Suggested questions/prompts:

- Talk to your partner about what you did to make sure you had found all the ways.
- What other ways could we investigate? What if there were four hens?

'Gazinta' puzzles: 1 and 2 (pages 26–27)

☆ *Processes: reason, look for pattern, record, co-operate, trial and improvement, check, explain, visualise*

The children will need to be familiar with ideas of division and know that one number can divide into another without a remainder. It might be useful to compile a list of division facts or multiples of the numbers 2, 3, 4, 5 and 10 to help the children with this work.

The children should observe that some numbers are related in many ways, whilst others are not.

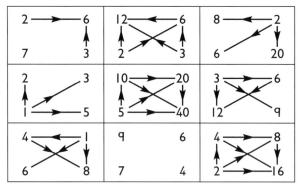

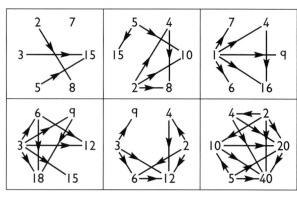

Suggested questions:

- What did you notice about these numbers?
- Which set of numbers had the most/fewest arrows?

Wheel meet again: 1 and 2 (pages 28–29)

☆ *Processes: look for pattern, ask own questions, be systematic, record, test ideas*

In this activity the children are encouraged to choose different rules and see what patterns are produced. Some might benefit from first drawing a table of results to help them draw the correct straight lines using a ruler.

Suggested questions:

- What pattern have you created for 'add 10'?
- What if you chose a different rule?
- What happens for larger numbers?
- Do you think you might have drawn one of your lines incorrectly? How could you check?

Solving problems

Morse code: 1 and 2 (pages 30–31)

☆ *Processes: be systematic, look for pattern, reason, trial and improvement*

In *Morse code: 1* the children are asked to find all the possible combinations for each number of sounds, and to look for patterns in the number of solutions found each time.

This is the full set of solutions:

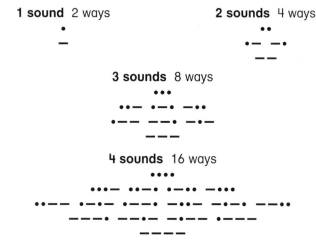

(The four not used in the international Morse code alphabet are: ———— ••—— ———• •—•—)

For the extension activity, the children should investigate their own ways of showing the digits 0 to 9 using five sounds. Do not provide them with *Morse code: 2* until they have designed their own way and are ready to compare and discuss which they think is most easy to remember and understand (which may of course be their own way!).

When using *Morse code: 2* for further investigation, encourage the children to notice that the letters which are used more frequently in everyday language are made using fewer sounds: for example, E and T have only one sound whereas Z and Q have four sounds. This could be linked to work on collecting data on the frequency of letters in a newspaper or magazine.

Three-letter words that could be investigated include words made from many sounds, such as FLY (12 sounds) or words made from the same number of sounds: for example, TIE, NET, TEA, MET, TEN, ATE, EAT (all four sounds).

Suggested questions:
- What patterns have you found?
- How can you be sure that you have found all the ways?
- Why do you think Z is four sounds and T is only one?

Permutation puzzles (page 32)
☆ *Processes: be systematic, record, generalise, look for pattern, compare, visualise, explain*

This task is designed to encourage the children to work systematically and persevere in order to find every permutation for a particular set. It encourages the children to see that, no matter what the context, the number of permutations when there are three items will always be the same (six).

As a further extension, the children could explore the number of different four-digit numbers that can be made using the digits 1, 2, 5 and 8.

Suggested questions/prompts:
- How is this order different from this? Are these two actually the same?
- How many ways did you find for this problem?
- Do you think you have found all the ways?
- Explain why you think there are the same number of solutions each time.

Hit the right note (page 33)
☆ *Processes: be systematic, generalise, compare, trial and improvement*

This activity leads on from the previous one (where children found the permutations of three items), by showing how the permutations of four items can be found in four separate stages. This is valuable in helping the children learn how to be systematic and in showing them that a task can be broken into simpler steps (simplifying).

The added benefit from this context is the cross-curricular link with music, in that children can create a tune made from each of the different permutations. (Note that it will sound best if the last note of the whole tune is the note C.)

Suggested questions:
- Did you find it helpful doing this in four separate groups?
- What did you notice about each of the groups?
- Did you use the answers to one group to help you with the next?

Counter intelligence (page 34)
☆ *Processes: co-operate, visualise, make decisions, reason, test ideas, trial and improvement*

The number of lines each circle lies along is as follows:

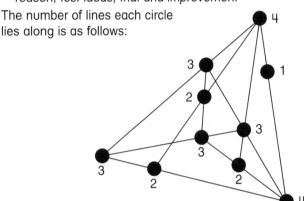

The children may begin to notice that it is best to start by placing a counter on a '4' circle. Encourage them to discuss their strategies and to play the game many times to develop a feel for what helps them to win.

Suggested questions/prompts:
- What strategies did you use?
- Does the first person always win?
- Which are the best positions to place your counters?
- Explain your thinking to your partner.

Trumpet tunes (page 35)
☆ *Processes: be systematic, generalise, look for pattern, compare*

Unlike the previous permutation activities, this involves finding all the ways that two or more trumpet keys could be positioned, either in the up (U) or down (D) positions. The number of solutions follows this pattern:

1 key	2 ways
2 keys	4 ways
3 keys	8 ways
4 keys	16 ways

and therefore 5 keys would be 32 ways, and so on.

The number of solutions follows the numbers in Pascal's triangle:

1 key 2 ways
U
D

2 keys 4 ways
UU
UD DU
DD

3 keys 8 ways
UUU
UUD UDU DUU
UDD DDU DUD
DDD

4 keys 16 ways
UUUU
UUUD UUDU UDUU DUUU
DDUU DUUD DUDU UDUD UDDU UUDD
DDDU DDUD DUDD UDDD
DDDD

- What have you noticed about the number of ways?
- What patterns did you notice?
- For four keys, how many ways did you find with one/two/three/four keys pressed down?

Magic keys: 1 and 2 (pages 36–37)

☆ *Processes: look for pattern, predict, test ideas, compare, make decisions, generalise*

The pattern on *Magic keys: 1* is as follows:

Number of chambers	3	4	5	6	7	8
Number run through	5	7	9	11	13	15

(The rule is double the number of chambers and subtract 1, although it is unlikely that you would choose to share this with children of this age.)

The children should spot that these are consecutive odd numbers, starting at 5. This will enable them to predict the following:

9	10	11	12
17	19	21	23

This activity can lead on to a wide range of further investigations.

Magic keys: 2 produces this pattern:

Number of rooms	4	6	8	10	12	14
Fewest number run through	5	6	9	10	13	14

The fewest number of rooms for multiples of 4 will be one more than the number of rooms. For non-multiples of 4, the fewest number will be the same as the number of rooms.

Suggested questions/prompts:

- What patterns do you notice?
- Explain your thinking to a partner.

Handling data

Telephone buttons (page 38)

☆ *Processes: record, test ideas, compare, ask own questions, generalise*

The children could display their findings on a poster to promote further discussion and interest. Graphs such as bar charts could be drawn using the data found.

Suggested questions/prompts:

- Explain to your partner what you notice.
- Why do you think this might be?
- How could you show what you have found on a poster?

Dotty domino patterns (page 39)

☆ *Processes: co-operate, look for pattern, predict, be systematic*

This activity can follow on from work on Venn diagrams with one and two criteria. It is essential that the children collaborate with a partner on this activity to promote

discussion and explanation of their thinking. Invite volunteers to describe the patterns they see to the class.

Further investigation work could include looking at the total number of dots on each domino and sorting them into groups with the same total. (This sheet could be enlarged so that the dominoes can be cut out and sorted.)

Suggested questions/prompts:

- Look at the rows and columns. How are the dominoes arranged?
- Explain to your partner what patterns you notice.

Measures, shape and space

Wands (page 40)

☆ *Processes: estimate, co-operate, predict, record, test ideas, check*

Estimating is a valuable using and applying skill and this activity encourages children to estimate lengths to the nearest half centimetre (for example, $4\frac{1}{2}$ cm or 7 cm).

The lengths of the wands are (to the nearest half centimetre):

A	9 cm
B	$13\frac{1}{2}$ cm
C	$4\frac{1}{2}$ cm
D	13 cm
E	11 cm
F	7 cm
G	15 cm
H	$8\frac{1}{2}$ cm
I	$3\frac{1}{2}$ cm
J	$5\frac{1}{2}$ cm
K	5 cm
L	$10\frac{1}{2}$ cm

If any children are able to measure lines to the nearest millimetre, group them in pairs and ask them to estimate the lengths and find the differences in millimetres. When photocopying the activity sheet for these children, the photocopier could be set to 96% so that the lengths of the wands are not whole centimetres or half centimetres.

Suggested questions:

- How good were your estimates?
- Did you get better each time you estimated?
- How far away was your estimate?

Time for a game (page 41)

☆ *Processes: estimate, co-operate, predict, record, test ideas, check*

Estimating is a valuable using and applying skill and this activity encourages the children to estimate time to the nearest second. Begin the lesson by discussing how long one second is, and demonstrate counting slowly (for example, 'one crocodile, two crocodiles, three crocodiles…'), to assist estimates.

Suggested questions:

- How good were your estimates?
- Did you get better each time you estimated?
- How far away was your estimate?

Hungry hamster (page 42)

☆ *Processes: record, visualise, make decisions, compare*

Let the children use their own way of recording, whether that be describing or drawing paths or shapes, or using words such as 'up', 'down', 'left' and 'right'. Once the instructions have been completed, ask the children to compare approaches and to say which ways they prefer and why. If appropriate, the children could be asked to do the activity a second time to see whether a more effective approach can be used.

Suggested questions:

- Whose instructions did you find easiest to understand?
- Why do you think that was?

Pampered pets (page 43)

☆ *Processes: reason, trial and improvement, visualise, look for pattern, check, compare*

Encourage the children to discuss their patterns and to explain their thinking to a partner. Children who undertake the extension activity should find that it is not possible to make a quilt with at least one square of each pattern that has two lines of symmetry.

Suggested questions:

- How is this pattern different from this one?
- If you turned this quilt upside down, would it be the same pattern as this one?

Helicopter pads: 1 and 2 (pages 44–45)

☆ *Processes: look for pattern, reason, explain, be systematic, generalise*

This activity encourages the children to carry out an experiment and to suggest reasons for the results. They could use different-coloured pencils to mark the routes. The possible routes to each of the pads follows the pattern called Pascal's triangle:

```
            1
          1   1
        1   2   1
      1   3   3   1
    1   4   6   4   1
```

On *Helicopter pads: 1*, the children should notice that the routes to the pads follow the pattern:

```
      1   2   1
```

Since each route is equally likely, it follows that you are twice as likely to land on pad 2 as on pad 1 or pad 3.

On *Helicopter pads: 2*, the routes follow the pattern:

```
      1   3   3   1
```

Suggested questions:

- Why do you think that you land on pad 2 more often than you land on pad 1?
- How many different routes are there to pad 2?

3-D puzzles (page 46)

☆ *Processes: visualise, predict, compare, test ideas*

Begin the lesson by taking a 3-D shape, such as a square-based pyramid, and drawing around the shape in different ways: for example, drawing around the square base of the pyramid and then around one of the triangular sides. Hold up other shapes and ask the children to visualise what shapes could be drawn on paper if you drew around the shape in different ways.

The following 3-D shapes are possibilities for the drawings on the activity sheet:

Circle: cylinder, cone or hemi-sphere
Square: cube, cuboid or square-based pyramid
Triangle: triangular prism or square-based pyramid
Rectangle: cuboid or triangular prism

The children could also argue that you can make a circle by drawing around a sphere, even though you would not be drawing around a face in the same way as drawing around the base of a cone. Encourage the children to explain and discuss their answers.

Suggested questions:

- Which shape could this be?
- Why do you think that?
- Are all cuboids the same?
- Could you have a cuboid with a square face, that is not a cube?

Letter lines (page 47)

☆ *Processes: visualise, predict, test ideas, explain*

This activity provides an opportunity for the children to practise visualising reflections of shapes in mirror lines.

Suggested questions:

- Which do you think will make a real letter/word?
- Which letter/word do you think it will make?
- Why do you think this?
- Can you think of other letters/words that we could reflect in the same way?

Leap and swap (page 48)

☆ *Processes: trial and improvement, reason, record, visualise, test ideas, be systematic*

The fewest number of moves possible is 15.

Suggested questions/prompts:

- How many moves did it take?
- Could you repeat that again?
- Think about how you could record the solution.

Wild about animals

Make predictions and test your ideas

Molly's bedroom has an animal border around the walls. This is one piece. Each piece is the same.

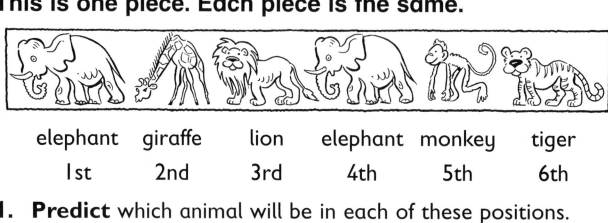

elephant	giraffe	lion	elephant	monkey	tiger
1st	2nd	3rd	4th	5th	6th

1. Predict which animal will be in each of these positions.

7th _elephant_   10th _____   13th _____

18th _____   20th _____   24th _____

Test your answers by counting on.

2. Write the first ten position numbers of these animals.

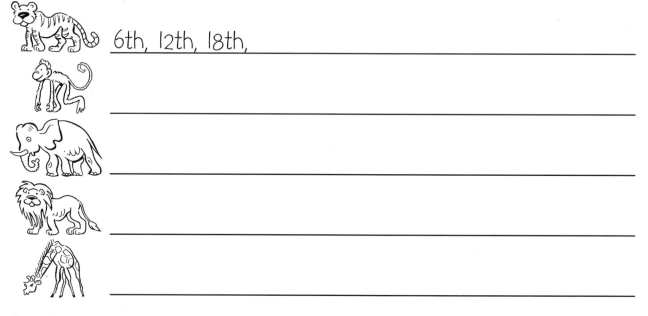

6th, 12th, 18th, _____

_____

_____

_____

_____

3. Use the patterns to help you predict which animal will be in

position: 72 _____   83 _____   112 _____

Now try this!

- **Make your own border with ⎡five⎤ animals.**
- **Predict which animal will be in position 99.**

Teachers' note Encourage the children to work with a partner and to discuss their predictions before testing them. Ensure they understand that their predictions can be checked by counting on from 7 as they point to each animal and returning to the first animal for 13, and so on. The sixth animal on the border could be masked, to provide easier patterns to explore. Ask the children to explain the patterns they see to the rest of the class.

Developing Numeracy
Using & Applying Maths
Year 3
© A & C BLACK

Star trekking

☆ Place the alien (counter) on **start**.

☆ Move the alien along the lines.
Every time the alien reaches a star
with a **multiple of 5** it loses a life (a cube).

You need a counter and five cubes.

☆ Can the alien reach **home** without losing all five lives?

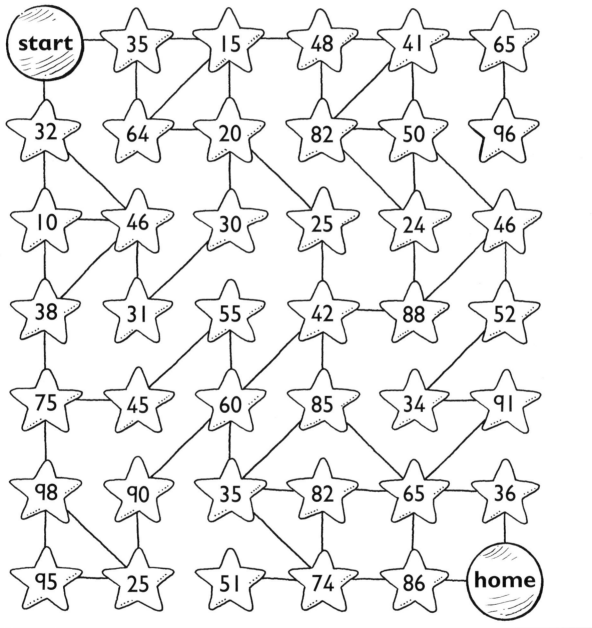

• Investigate which route has the `most` **multiples of 5.**

Now try this!

Honey, I'm home!

Teachers' note This activity helps the children to develop perseverance. Encourage them to try the puzzle again and again, trying out different routes. They may find it helpful to use coloured pencils to mark routes they have tried. There are several ways of reaching 'home' without losing all five lives. For the extension activity, children may require a clean copy of the sheet. Tell them that they should not visit the same star more than once.

Developing Numeracy
Using & Applying Maths
Year 3
© A & C BLACK

Half-time scores

Look for patterns and explain your findings

The school football team won a match $1:0$.
The two possible scores at half-time
are $0:0$ and $1:0$.

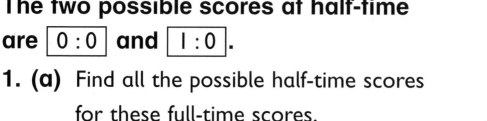

1. (a) Find all the possible half-time scores
for these full-time scores.

$0:0$	0 : 0
$1:0$	0 : 0 1 : 0
$2:0$	
$3:0$	
$4:0$	
$5:0$	

(b) How many possible half-time scores do you <u>think</u> there
are for this full-time score? $9:0$ _____

2. (a) Find all the possible half-time scores for these
full-time scores.

$1:1$	
$2:2$	
$3:3$	

(b) Talk to a partner about the number of ways you found.

Now try this! • **Choose other full-time
score-draws to investigate.**

Teachers' note Encourage the children to notice and explain patterns in the number of possible
half-time scores they found for different full-time scores. At particular moments in the lesson, stop the
class and ask the children to talk in pairs for two minutes about their work and what they have found.
Invite volunteers to describe the patterns they have found to the whole class. For the extension
activity, check that the children know that score-draws are 1 : 1, 2 : 2, 3 : 3, and so on.

**Developing Numeracy
Using & Applying Maths
Year 3
© A & C BLACK**

16

Digit riddles

A secret number is describing itself.

I have two digits that are the same.
I am between 0 and 200.

- **On the number grid below, ring all the possible numbers it could be.**

1	2	3	4	5	6	7	8	9	10
(11)	12	13	14	15	16	17	18	19	20
21	22	23	24	25	26	27	28	29	30
31	32	33	34	35	36	37	38	39	40
41	42	43	44	45	46	47	48	49	50
51	52	53	54	55	56	57	58	59	60
61	62	63	64	65	66	67	68	69	70
71	72	73	74	75	76	77	78	79	80
81	82	83	84	85	86	87	88	89	90
91	92	93	94	95	96	97	98	99	100
101	102	103	104	105	106	107	108	109	110
111	112	113	114	115	116	117	118	119	120
121	122	123	124	125	126	127	128	129	130
131	132	133	134	135	136	137	138	139	140
141	142	143	144	145	146	147	148	149	150
151	152	153	154	155	156	157	158	159	160
161	162	163	164	165	166	167	168	169	170
171	172	173	174	175	176	177	178	179	180
181	182	183	184	185	186	187	188	189	190
191	192	193	194	195	196	197	198	199	200

Clue
There are three times as many possible numbers between 100 and 200 as there are between 0 and 100.

- **Colour all the ringed numbers with only**

  odd **digits. Example: 111**

Teachers' note The children should be encouraged to notice and describe patterns in the numbers they circle. For further investigations, the riddle could be masked and a new one written in its place: for example, 'I am between 0 and 200 and have digits that when added together make 7.' (Any number up to 19 can be used for the total.)

**Developing Numeracy
Using & Applying Maths
Year 3
© A & C BLACK**

On the buses

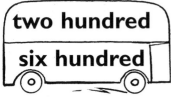

two hundred **six hundred**   **forty** **thirty**   **five** **seven**

- **Use the number names on the buses to make as many different numbers as you can. Write them in the correct group.**

Numbers less than 100

forty-five
45

Numbers greater than 100

six hundred and seven
607

two hundred and thirty-five
235

- **What if you could also use** one thousand **?**
How many more numbers could you make?

Teachers' note This activity provides an opportunity for the children to practise reading and writing numbers in words and figures in an open way. The children are likely to ask whether they can include single numbers such as 40 and 5. Encourage them to make their own decision, as this will help to steer them away from the idea that there is only one correct way of doing things.

**Developing Numeracy
Using & Applying Maths
Year 3
© A & C BLACK**

18

A space oddity

Generalise, make predictions and check

- **Write all the** | odd | **numbers between** | 10 | **and** | 20 |.

_____

- **How many are there?** _____

- **Now write all the odd numbers between:**

  20 and 30 _____

  30 and 40 _____

  40 and 50 _____

  50 and 60 _____

- **Write three things that you notice.**

_____

_____

_____

- **Predict how many odd numbers there are between** | 0 | **and** | 100 |. _____

  Use what you have noticed.

- **Check your prediction by counting the odd numbers.**

  You will need a 100-square.

Now try this!

- **Predict how many odd numbers there are between** | 0 | **and** | 1000 |. _____
- **How can you check your prediction? Explain to a partner.**

?

Teachers' note Whilst there are several ways of generalising the number of odd numbers between 0 and 100 (for example, knowing that for every odd number there is an even number), this approach focuses on the number of odd numbers in each 'decade'. Encourage the children to reach their own conclusions without too much assistance, and then to explain and discuss their work with a partner.

**Developing Numeracy
Using & Applying Maths
Year 3
© A & C BLACK**

- **On the fingernails of one hand,**

  write the numbers 1, 2, 4, 8 and 16.

  Different totals can be made.

Example: 1 + 2 = 3   1 + 2 + 4 = 7

- **Place your hand flat on the table.**

  Which totals from 1 to 30 can you make?

1	1	16	
2	2	17	
3	1 + 2	18	
4	4	19	
5	1 + 4	20	
6	2 + 4	21	
7	1 + 2 + 4	22	
8		23	
9		24	
10		25	
11		26	
12		27	
13		28	
14		29	
15		30	

- **Imagine you had a sixth finger, labelled 32 .**

  Make all the totals from 31 to 60 .

Teachers' note The children should label their non-writing hand and number the fingers from left to right. (Numbers can be written in pencil and wiped off later.) Ensure the children understand that they can use any number of fingers, but each finger only once. Ask them to describe any patterns they notice to a partner as they work. A complete class list of solutions could be displayed. Encourage the children to notice that each number is double the number to its left.

Developing Numeracy
Using & Applying Maths
Year 3
© A & C BLACK

20

Total teaser: 2

You need the chart you completed on *Total teaser: 1.*

☆ Take each total in turn. Write them onto the cards below, like this:

3 is **1 + 2**, so write 3 on the cards labelled 1 and 2.

5 is **1 + 4**, so write 5 on the cards labelled 1 and 4.

6 is **2 + 4**, so write 6 on the cards labelled 2 and 4.

7 is **1 + 2 + 4**, so write 7 on the cards labelled 1, 2 and 4.

☆ Continue <u>in order</u>, up to 30.

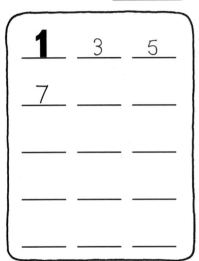
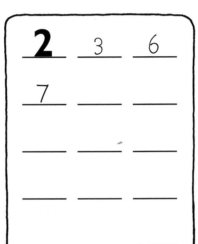
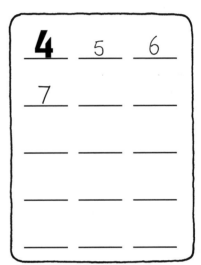

- **Talk to a partner about the patterns in the numbers on each card.**

- **Cut out the cards. Your teacher will explain how to perform a magic trick with them.**

Teachers' note If the children have not completed page 20, as a class explore how any whole number up to 30 can be made by using or adding together the following numbers: 1, 2, 4, 8 and 16. Compile a class list of solutions (see page 8) for the children to refer to. Encourage them to notice patterns of odd and even or consecutive numbers on the cards. For the extension activity, refer to page 8 for an explanation of how to perform the magic trick.

Developing Numeracy
Using & Applying Maths
Year 3
© A & C BLACK

Terrific tiles

Reason and make decisions

There are three types of tiles in a shop.

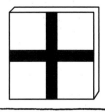  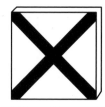

10p per tile   12p per tile   15p per tile

Mrs Barker is choosing nine tiles to put in a line above her bath. She wants the design to have two lines of symmetry.

Example:

- **Draw some designs. Then work out how much each design would cost.**

- **Investigate whether it is possible to make designs that cost exactly:**

  95p   £1   £1.20   £1.01   93p   99p

You need squared paper.

Teachers' note Ensure the children understand that the pattern should be symmetrical vertically about the middle of the centre tile. Encourage them to use reasoning when answering the questions, talking to a partner when appropriate. See page 9 for further notes.

Developing Numeracy Using & Applying Maths Year 3 © A & C BLACK

Lily pads

Look for patterns and make comparisons

Nine lily pads are numbered $\boxed{10}$ **to** $\boxed{90}$.

- **Draw lines to join lily pads with:**

a difference of 30

a difference of 40

a difference of 50

a difference of 60

a difference of 70

a difference of 80

- **How many lines did you draw for a difference of:**

30? $\boxed{6}$ 40? $\boxed{}$ 50? $\boxed{}$ 60? $\boxed{}$ 70? $\boxed{}$ 80? $\boxed{}$

- **Talk to a partner about what you notice.**

Now try this!

- **Join pairs of lily pads which have a** $\boxed{\text{total of 100}}$.
- **Draw your own lily pads. Try other totals between 30 and 120.**

(10) (20) (30)

(40) (50) (60)

(70) (80) (90)

Teachers' note This activity encourages the children to explore and compare different patterns made by lines when joining numbers with particular differences or totals. Show the children how looking for patterns can help them to check that they have found all the solutions: for example, if one line is missed on the 'difference of 50' diagram, then the pattern of lines would be 6, 5, **3**, 3, 2, 1, drawing attention to a missing line.

Developing Numeracy
Using & Applying Maths
Year 3
© A & C BLACK

23

Piles of coins

You need 12 coins of the same value.

- ## Follow these rules.

Place 5 coins here: Place 7 coins here:

☆ Look at the pile with the **smaller number** of coins. Double the number on this pile by taking that number of coins off the larger pile.

☆ Look at the pile that has the **smaller number** of coins now. Double the number on this pile by taking that number of coins off the larger pile.

☆ Keep going like this and see what happens. Record your results on a sheet of paper.

- ## Follow the rules above for these starting piles.

Place 11 coins here: Place 1 coin here:

Place 2 coins here: Place 10 coins here:

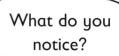

What do you notice?

- ## Try other starting piles, such as 9 and 3.
- ## Try using a different number of coins altogether, such as 10, 9 or 8. Talk to a partner about what you notice.

Teachers' note In this investigation the question 'What is double zero?' might arise. Discuss that zero doubled is zero and so no more moves can be made. See page 9 for more about the patterns that arise in this investigation. As an extension activity, the children could design a poster showing what they have found out. Encourage them to describe any patterns they notice.

Developing Numeracy
Using & Applying Maths
Year 3
© A & C BLACK

Eggs in nests

Be systematic and make comparisons

Every day, three hens lay up to 2 eggs each. Each hen could lay no eggs , 1 egg or 2 eggs .

• **Find all the ways of arranging the eggs. Write the total each time.**

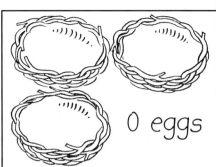

0 eggs

1 egg

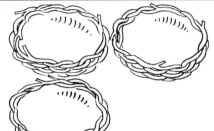

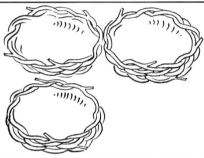

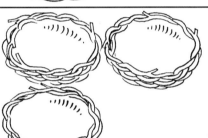

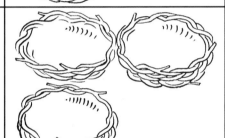

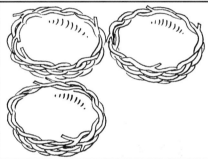

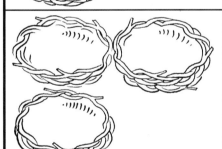

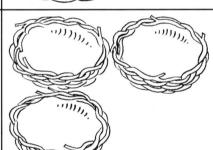

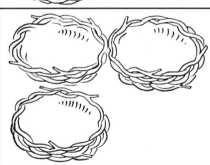

• **Write the totals in order.**

What patterns can you see?

_____

Now try this!

• **Find all the possible ways if the three hens lay up to 3 eggs each.**

• **Write your totals in order.** Look for patterns.

Teachers' note Discuss ways of working systematically, starting with no eggs in any of the nests and changing one nest at a time. Then move on to finding ways with 1 egg in the first nest, then 2 eggs, being careful to check that each solution is not one already found. Ensure the children understand that the order of the eggs does not matter: for example, 1, 2 and 0 is the same as 0, 1 and 2. See pages 9 and 10 for solutions.

**Developing Numeracy
Using & Applying Maths
Year 3
© A & C BLACK**

Reason

You can draw arrows between numbers to show which number 'goes into' another without a remainder.

3 ———————→ 15
3 goes into 15

or

2

8

2 goes into 8

You could not draw an arrow between 4 and 7 because 4 does not go into 7 without a remainder.

• Draw all the arrows you can between these numbers.

You can join two or more arrows to the same number.

2 ——→ 6	12	6	8	2
7	3	2	3	6	20
2	3	10	20	3	6
1	5	5	40	12	9
4	1	9	6	4	8
6	8	7	4	2	16

• With a partner, discuss which numbers have most arrows going to them. Why is this?

• Make up your own 'gazinta' puzzles. Can you make a puzzle with exactly four arrows?

Teachers' note Ensure the children realise that the direction of the arrow is important in showing which number goes into another, and encourage them to work systematically. The word 'gazinta' is a pun on the phrase 'goes into'. More confident children could tackle page 27.

**Developing Numeracy
Using & Applying Maths
Year 3
© A & C BLACK**

26

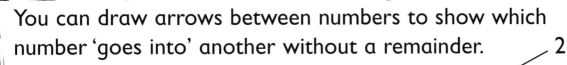

Reason

You can draw arrows between numbers to show which number 'goes into' another without a remainder.

3 ———————→ 15
3 goes into 15

or

2

8

2 goes into 8

You could not draw an arrow between 4 and 7 because 4 does not go into 7 without a remainder.

• Draw all the arrows you can between these numbers.

You can join two or more arrows to the same number.

2 7	5 4	7 4
3 15	15 10	1 9
5 8	2 8	6 16
6 9	9 4	4 2
3 12	3 2	10 20
18 15	6 12	5 40

• With a partner, discuss which numbers have most arrows going to them. Why is this?

• Make up your own 'gazinta' puzzles. Make a puzzle with as many arrows as you can.

Now try this!

Teachers' note This page could be tackled by children who have successfully completed page 26. Ensure the children realise that the direction of the arrow is important in showing which number goes into another, and encourage them to work systematically.

Developing Numeracy Using & Applying Maths Year 3 © A & C BLACK

Wheel meet again: 1

- **Follow the instructions for this rule:** add 10 .

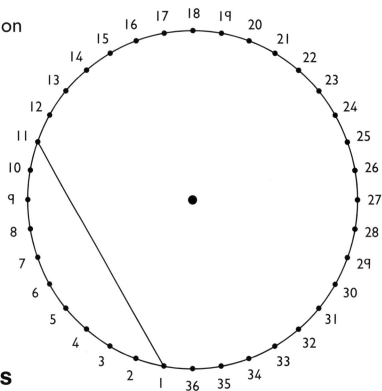

☆ **Add 10** to each number on the wheel. Start at 1 and do each number in turn. Use a ruler to draw a line from the number to the answer.

☆ When you reach 27, continue the pattern of lines.

☆ Talk to a partner about what you notice.

- **Try out different rules using *Wheel meet again: 2.***

Now try this!

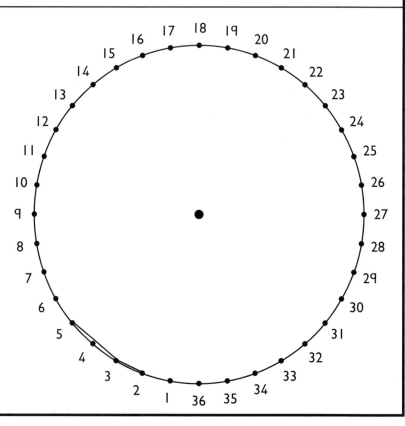

- **Use this rule:**

double, then subtract 1

- **Continue the pattern for the rest of the numbers.**

Teachers' note The children will need a copy of page 29 to explore their own wheel patterns. Some children may find continuing the pattern in the extension activity more difficult. Encourage them to look carefully at where the lines start and end.

**Developing Numeracy
Using & Applying Maths
Year 3
© A & C BLACK**

Wheel meet again: 2

Look for patterns and ask your own questions

• Make up your own rules. Draw the wheel patterns.

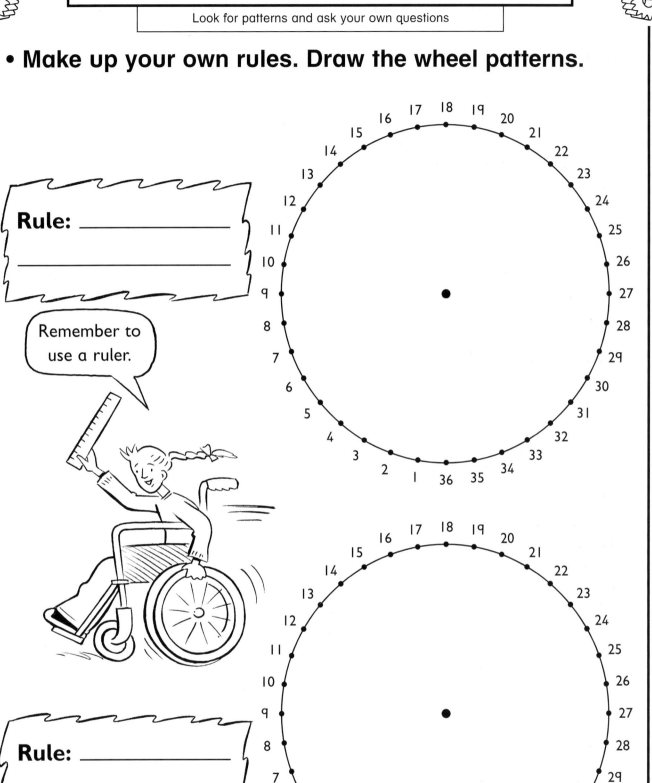

Rule: _____

_____

Remember to use a ruler.

Rule: _____

_____

Teachers' note Use this with the activity on page 28. Encourage the children to predict what a pattern might look like before testing their ideas.

**Developing Numeracy
Using & Applying Maths
Year 3
© A & C BLACK**

29

Be systematic

Morse code is a way of sending messages using short and long sounds.

A short sound is written as a dot, like this •

A long sound is written as a dash, like this —

Each letter of the alphabet is written as one, two, three or four sounds. For example:

A is 'short, long'   T is 'long'   S is 'short, short, short'

• —   —   • • •

• **Show all the possible ways of making:**

One sound	• —

There are only two ways of making one sound.

Two sounds

Three sounds

Four sounds

Now try this!

The digits 0 to 9 are all made using five sounds.

• **Design your own code for these digits.**

Make sure they are easy to remember.

Teachers' note Begin by introducing Morse code as a way of communicating. When the children are completing the sheet, encourage them to find all the solutions for each number of sounds and to look for patterns in the number of solutions found each time. (See page 10 for more information.) Ask questions such as: 'Have you found all the ways? Are there enough for each letter of the alphabet?' Page 31 can be given to the children *after* they have completed the extension activity.

Developing Numeracy
Using & Applying Maths
Year 3
© A & C BLACK

Morse code: 2

Look for patterns

- **This is the international Morse code.**

A	• —	**N**	— •	full stop	• — • — • —
B	— • • •	**O**	— — —	comma	— — • • — —
C	— • — •	**P**	• — — •	query	• • — — • •
D	— • •	**Q**	— — • —	**0**	— — — — —
E	•	**R**	• — •	**1**	• — — — —
F	• • — •	**S**	• • •	**2**	• • — — —
G	— — •	**T**	—	**3**	• • • — —
H	• • • •	**U**	• • —	**4**	• • • • —
I	• •	**V**	• • • —	**5**	• • • • •
J	• — — —	**W**	• — —	**6**	— • • • •
K	— • —	**X**	— • • —	**7**	— — • • •
L	• — • •	**Y**	— • — —	**8**	— — — • •
M	— —	**Z**	— — • •	**9**	— — — — •

- **List the letters which have one sound. Then list those with two sounds, three sounds, and so on.**

Why do you think they have been made this way?

Now try this!

- **Write some three-letter words in Morse code.**
- **How many sounds do they use? Which words use the most and fewest sounds?**

Teachers' note The children should first complete the activity on page 30. Ask them whether they found any sound combinations on *Morse code: 1* that are not used in the international Morse code (there are four; see page 10). In the extension activity, encourage the children to find variations in the number of sounds used in different three-letter words: for example, 'ant' is made using five sounds, whereas 'cow' is made using ten sounds.

Developing Numeracy
Using & Applying Maths
Year 3
© A & C BLACK

Permutation puzzles

• Find all the solutions for each puzzle.

1. On this car registration plate, the letters **B**, **M** and **E** are covered in mud. Find all the ways the letters could go.

YL05 ✦✦✦

B M E   B E M   _____

_____   _____   _____

2. Show all the ways these children could stand in a line.

A B C, _____

_____

3. Find all the three-digit numbers that can be made from these three cards.

$$2 \quad 4 \quad 7$$

247, _____

_____

4. Write all the different orders that Jo can say these words:

pip pop pup

pip pop pup, _____

_____

5. Show all the ways that Marvo can put these three cups in a line.

Red Blue Pink Marvo

R B P, _____

_____

6. Three shapes are in a line. Draw all the ways that they could be arranged.

□ ○ △, _____

_____

Teachers' note The children do not necessarily need to know the word 'permutation' (all possible arrangements of items in a set), but it can provide a label for useful discussion of these ideas and serve as a reminder when future work of this kind is attempted. As an extension, the children could discuss with a partner the number of solutions for each puzzle, and possible reasons for this. See page 11 for a further extension.

Developing Numeracy Using & Applying Maths Year 3 © A & C BLACK

Hit the right note

Each of these chime bars is struck once. The bars can be struck in any order.

• Find all the ways the bars can be struck when:

1. C is struck first.

C _E_ _G_ _A_   C __ __ __   C __ __ __

C __ __ __   C __ __ __   C __ __ __

2. E is struck first.

E __ __ __   E __ __ __   E __ __ __

E __ __ __   E __ __ __   E __ __ __

3. G is struck first.

G __ __ __   G __ __ __   G __ __ __

G __ __ __   G __ __ __   G __ __ __

4. A is struck first.

A __ __ __   A __ __ __   A __ __ __

A __ __ __   A __ __ __   A __ __ __

• How many ways is this altogether? _____

• Play each set of notes above, one after the other, to make a tune.

You need chime bars **or** a xylophone **or** a glockenspiel.

Teachers' note This activity encourages the children to tackle an investigation systematically, by asking them to work from one starting note at a time. Some children will begin to notice that, to an extent, they can use one set of answers to help them find the next (for example, by swapping over all the Cs and Es). The extension activity lets the children use the results for a purpose and reinforces the idea that careful recording and interpreting is valuable. Provide suitable musical instruments.

Developing Numeracy
Using & Applying Maths
Year 3
© A & C BLACK

Counter intelligence

Co-operate, visualise and make decisions

• **Play this game with a partner.**

You need ten small counters, five in one colour and five in a different colour.

☆ Take turns to place a counter on a circle.

☆ The first player to get three on a straight line wins!

☆ Play again. Take turns to go first.

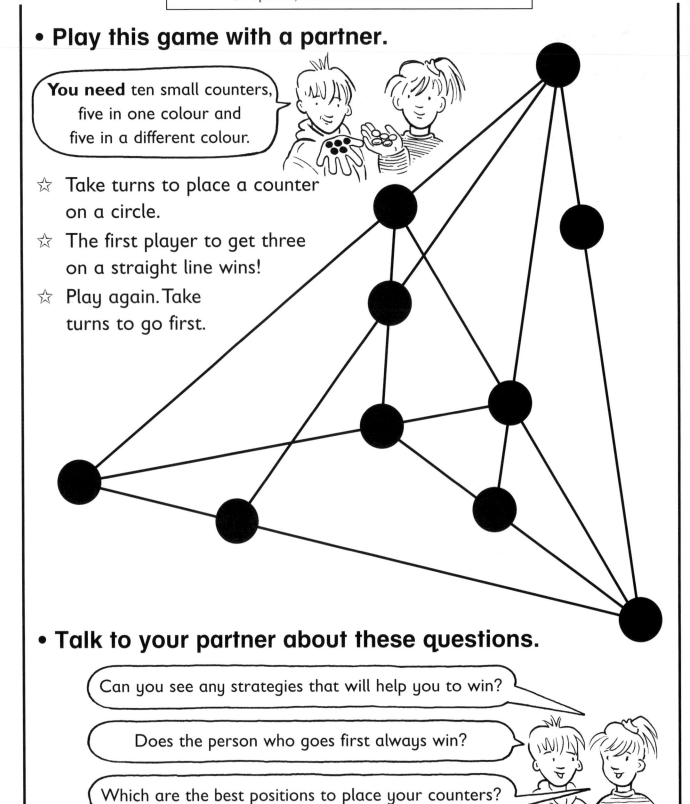

• **Talk to your partner about these questions.**

Can you see any strategies that will help you to win?

Does the person who goes first always win?

Which are the best positions to place your counters?

• **Draw your own three-in-a-line game.**

Teachers' note Cubes can be used instead of counters. When discussing strategies, encourage the children to look at the number of lines each circle lies along: for example, it may lie along only one line, whereas some lie along two, three or four lines. When the children design their own games, ask them to start by drawing a large basic shape, such as a square, and then to draw dots at the corners and add further lines. They must make sure that only three circles appear along any one line.

**Developing Numeracy
Using & Applying Maths
Year 3
© A & C BLACK**

Trumpet tunes

A toy trumpet has two **keys.**
Each key can be up U **or down** D .
Here are all the different positions
the two keys can be in.

U U   U D   D U   D D

This trumpet has three **keys.**
• **Find all the different positions**
   for the three keys.

U U U   _____   _____

_____   _____   _____

This trumpet has four **keys!**
• **Find all the different positions**
   for the four keys.

U U U U   _____   _____

_____   _____   _____

_____   _____   _____

_____   _____   _____

• **Count the number of ways you found for:**

two keys 4   three keys ☐   four keys ☐

Now try this!

• **Predict the number of ways**
   for five **keys.** ☐

How can you check
your prediction?

Teachers' note Discuss ways of working systematically, such as finding all the different ways where
only one key is down, then where two keys are down, and so on. Counting the number of solutions in
each set can help to identify any missing solutions. See page 11 for more information on this pattern.

Developing Numeracy
Using & Applying Maths
Year 3
© **A & C BLACK**

35

Magic keys: 1

☆ In each chamber of a secret passage there is a magic key. To free the princess, the prince must run through the passage, collect **all** the keys and run back out the way he came in.

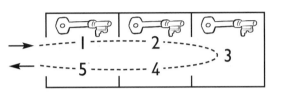

☆ This secret passage has three chambers. The number of chambers he must run through (there and back) is **five**.

• **Fill in the table to show the number of chambers the prince must run through for these passages.**

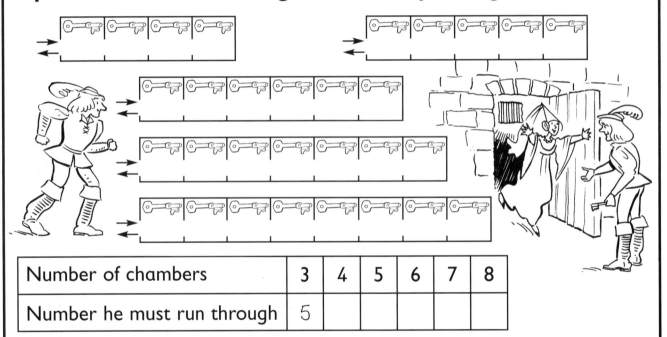

Number of chambers	3	4	5	6	7	8
Number he must run through	5					

• **Predict the number of chambers the prince must run through for a passage with:**

9 chambers   10 chambers   11 chambers   12 chambers

☐   ☐   ☐   ☐

• **Test your predictions.**

Teachers' note Ensure the children understand that the prince must enter and leave the passage by the same doorway, and that they should count the number of chambers he must run through there and back (for example, in a passage with two chambers he must run through three chambers in order to collect the keys and then leave the passage). Provide squared paper for the extension activity. The activity on page 37 can be used to explore these ideas further.

**Developing Numeracy
Using & Applying Maths
Year 3
© A & C BLACK**

Magic keys: 2

Look for patterns and make predictions

☆ In each room of a dungeon there is a magic key. To free the prince, the princess must run through the dungeon, collect **all** the keys and run out through the exit.

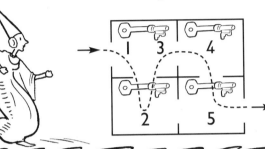

☆ This dungeon has four rooms. The fewest number of rooms she must run through is **five**.

• **Fill in the table to show the** fewest **number of rooms she must run through for these dungeons.**

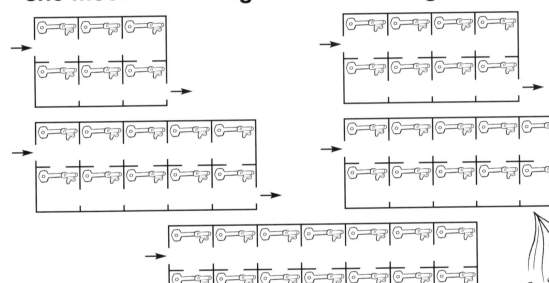

Number of rooms	4	6	8	10	12	14
Fewest number she must run through	5					

What do you notice about the dungeons with 6, 10 or 14 rooms?

Now try this!

• **Investigate dungeons with different arrangements of rooms, like this:**

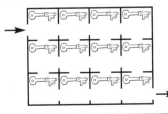

Teachers' note This leads on from the activity on page 36. Ensure the children understand that they must count the number of rooms the princess must run through in order to collect the keys and then leave the dungeon. Encourage the children to describe in words any patterns they notice (for example, to explain what they notice about dungeons with rooms that are multiples of 4).

**Developing Numeracy
Using & Applying Maths
Year 3
© A & C BLACK**

Telephone buttons

Which button on a
telephone is pressed
most often?

**Your teacher will give you some phone
numbers from the telephone book.**

- **Go through and count the number
  of times that each digit appears
  in the numbers. Keep a tally.**

0	
1	
2	
3	
4	
5	
6	
7	
8	
9	

- **Which button do you think
  will wear out most quickly?** ☐

Now try this!

- **Use a different set of phone numbers.
  Do you get the same results?**

Teachers' note Provide each child with a small section of a page from an old telephone book. The
number of telephone numbers given should be appropriate to the ability of the child. Encourage the
children to make a prediction before undertaking the activity, and to see whether their prediction is
correct. Discussion and further investigation could also take place about whether the results will be
the same in different areas of the country.

**Developing Numeracy
Using & Applying Maths
Year 3
© A & C BLACK**

Dotty domino patterns

Co-operate and look for patterns

- **Work with a partner.**
- **Look at the patterns of dots on these dominoes.**

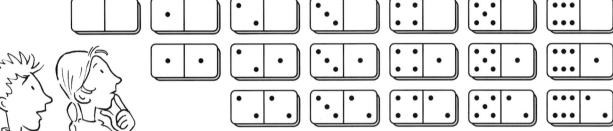

The dots in this row are missing. ⟶

- **Fill in the dots.**

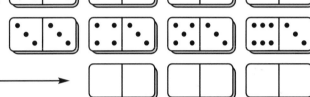

- **Cover up the top row of dominoes.**
- **Draw the rest of the dominoes on this** | Venn diagram |.

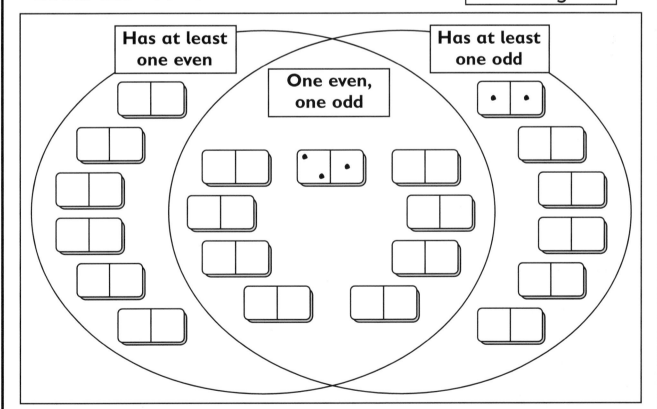

Teachers' note As pairs of children look at the patterns of dots, draw the class together and ask: 'How are the dominoes arranged? What do you notice about the left-hand side of the dominoes in a column? What do you notice about the right-hand side?' Before completing the Venn diagram, the children should cover the top row of dominoes with a ruler (or cross them out). As an extension, the children could explore patterns in the total number of dots on the dominoes in each column.

**Developing Numeracy
Using & Applying Maths
Year 3
© A & C BLACK**

Wands

Make estimates and co-operate with others

• **Play this game with a partner.**

You need a ruler.

☆ Take turns to choose a wand. **Estimate** its length to the nearest half centimetre, for example 4 cm.

☆ Your partner checks your estimate by measuring the wand to the nearest half centimetre, for example $4\frac{1}{2}$ cm.

☆ Work out the **difference** between your estimate and the actual length. This is your score, for example $\frac{1}{2}$ point.

☆ The winner is the player with the **lowest** score at the end.

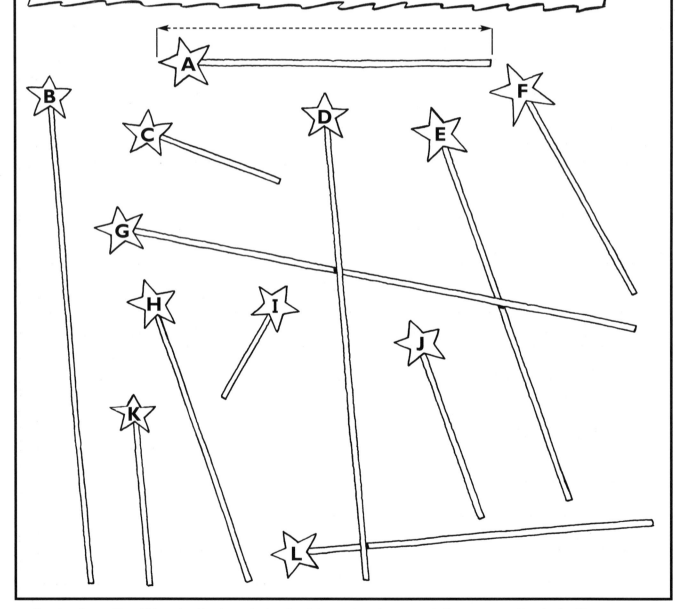

Teachers' note The children should estimate the lengths of the wands to the nearest half centimetre. Ask them to record on scrap paper the letter of the wand, their estimate, the actual length and the difference, to keep score. Draw this in table form on the board for them to copy at the start of the lesson. As an extension, the children could draw their own wands game for another pair to play.

Developing Numeracy
Using & Applying Maths
Year 3
© A & C BLACK

Time for a game

Make estimates and co-operate with others

• **Play this game with a partner.**

> **You need** a stopwatch.

☆ Player 2: start the stopwatch and say 'Start'.

☆ Player 1: read the first target in your table and estimate that length of time. Say 'Stop' when you think the time is up.

☆ Player 2: stop the stopwatch and read out what it says.

☆ Player 1: work out the **difference** between the target and your estimate. This is your score.

☆ Swap over so that Player 1 has the stopwatch. Keep playing.

☆ The winner is the player with the **lowest total** score.

Player 1

Target	Estimate	Difference (score)
24 seconds		
39 seconds		
12 seconds		
47 seconds		
59 seconds		
27 seconds		
Total		

Player 2

Target	Estimate	Difference (score)
23 seconds		
48 seconds		
36 seconds		
15 seconds		
54 seconds		
60 seconds		
Total		

Teachers' note Provide stopwatches for this activity. Each pair needs a stopwatch and one copy of the activity sheet. Introduce the game by letting all the children estimate a duration of 30 seconds. Ask them to close their eyes. Start a stopwatch and say 'start'. When the children think the time is up, they should put up their hand and open their eyes. As an extension, the children could repeat the game using target times between one minute and two minutes.

Developing Numeracy
Using & Applying Maths
Year 3
© A & C BLACK

Hungry hamster

☆ The hamster needs to collect **all** the sunflower seeds in the maze and then leave through the exit.

☆ **Without drawing on the maze**, choose a route for the hamster. Write instructions for your route so that someone else can follow it.

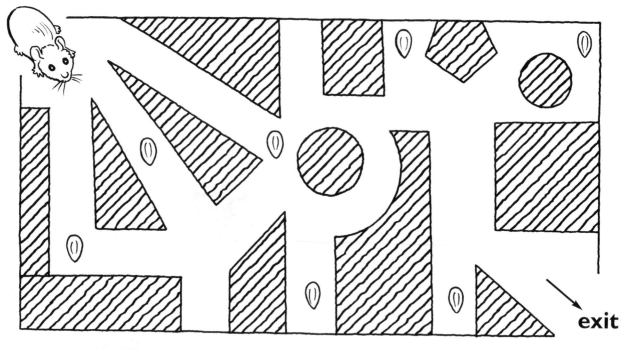

exit

My instructions

Now try this!

• **Swap sheets with a partner. Can you follow each other's routes?**

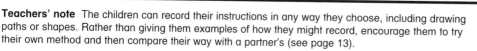

Teachers' note The children can record their instructions in any way they choose, including drawing paths or shapes. Rather than giving them examples of how they might record, encourage them to try their own method and then compare their way with a partner's (see page 13).

Developing Numeracy
Using & Applying Maths
Year 3
© A & C BLACK

42

Pampered pets

☆ Each square of a pet quilt has **spots** or **stripes** or **checks**.

☆ Each quilt has at least one square of each pattern.

☆ No squares are left blank.

☆ Every quilt pattern has at least **one line of symmetry**.

• **Find as many different quilt patterns as you can.**

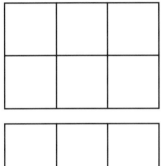 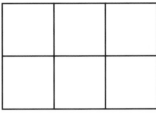 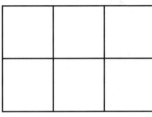

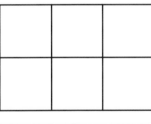 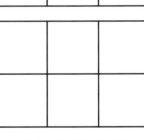 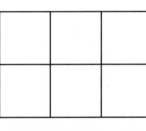

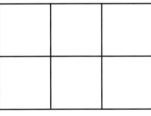 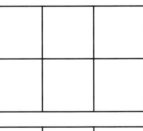 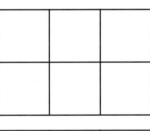

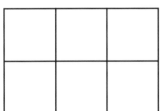 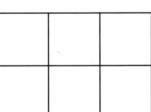 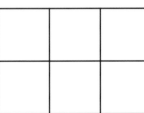

 Are any of your patterns the same but upside down?

 Now try this!

• **Do any of your patterns have** | two lines of symmetry |? Find out if it is possible.

Teachers' note Encourage the children to realise that the quilt could have a line of symmetry going horizontally or one going vertically through the middle of the two middle squares. Suggest that they work on patterns with a vertical line of symmetry, before moving on to the horizontal one. For the extension activity, remind the children that the quilt should have at least one square of each pattern.

**Developing Numeracy
Using & Applying Maths
Year 3
© A & C BLACK**

Helicopter pads: 1

Look for patterns

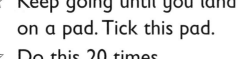

You need a counter and a coin.

☆ Place the counter on the helicopter. Toss the coin.
   Heads – move the counter down to the left.
   Tails – move down to the right.

☆ Keep going until you land on a pad. Tick this pad.

☆ Do this 20 times.

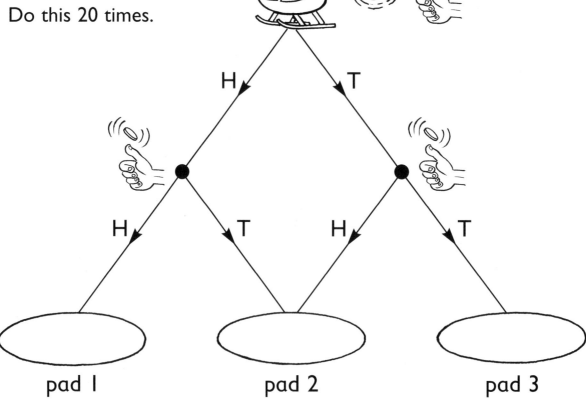

pad 1   pad 2   pad 3

- **Which pad do you land on most often?** _____

- **Why do you think this is?**

_____

_____

_____

Now try this!

- **What do you think would happen if you did the test 40 times? Explain your answer.**
- **Do the test and see whether you were right.**

Teachers' note Encourage the children to notice that there are more ways of reaching pad 2 than of reaching pads 1 and 3. Help them to trace the different routes with their fingers. See page 13 for more information about the patterns and reasons behind them.

**Developing Numeracy
Using & Applying Maths
Year 3
© A & C BLACK**

Helicopter pads: 2

Look for patterns

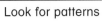

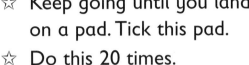

You need a counter and a coin.

☆ Place the counter on the helicopter. Toss the coin.
   Heads – move the counter down to the left.
   Tails – move down to the right.

☆ Keep going until you land on a pad. Tick this pad.

☆ Do this 20 times.

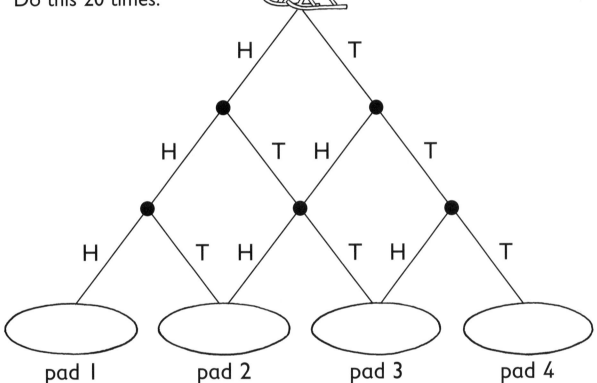

pad 1   pad 2   pad 3   pad 4

- **Which pads do you land on most often?** _____

- **On the back of this sheet, explain why this might be.**

- **Test your idea by counting how many different ways the helicopter could reach:**

pad 1 ____   pad 2 ____   pad 3 ____   pad 4 ____

Now try this!

- **Draw your own helicopter diagram. This time have four levels before you reach the pads.**
- **What do you notice this time?**

Teachers' note This sheet can be used to extend the activity on page 44. Encourage the children to notice that there are more ways of reaching pads 2 and 3 than of reaching pads 1 and 4. Help them to trace the different routes with their fingers. See page 13 for more information about the patterns and reasons behind them.

Developing Numeracy
Using & Applying Maths
Year 3
© A & C BLACK

3-D puzzles

Jo put some 3-D shapes onto paper and drew round them.

Here are the shapes I used.

cube
cuboid
square-based
    pyramid
cone
triangular prism
sphere
hemi-sphere
cylinder

Below are some of Jo's drawings.

• Which of the shapes could each be?

There might be more than one answer.

It could be the:

cylinder or cone or

_____

_____

It could be the:

_____

_____

_____

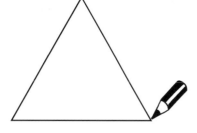

It could be the:

_____

_____

_____

It could be the:

_____

_____

_____

Teachers' note Demonstrate this activity practically using real 3-D shapes (see page 13). Some children may need a set of the 3-D shapes listed above when working on this activity, although they should be encouraged to visualise the shapes in their heads where possible. As an extension, ask the children to draw round 3-D shapes to make their own puzzle for a partner to solve.

Developing Numeracy
Using & Applying Maths
Year 3
© A & C BLACK

Letter lines

- **Here are halves of some letters. Tick the ones you <u>think</u> will make real letters when you put a mirror on the dotted line.**

☐   ☐   ☐

- **Now use a mirror to check.**

- **Which of these do you think will make real words?**

☐   ☐   ☐

- **Now use a mirror to check.**

- **Investigate other words that work in this way.**

Write your words here.

- **Investigate which letters have more than one line of symmetry. How many real words can you make with them?**

Now try this!

Teachers' note Provide mirrors once the children have made their prediction and discussed it with a partner. For the extension activity, the children could use a dictionary to check whether they have made real words.

**Developing Numeracy
Using & Applying Maths
Year 3
© A & C BLACK**

Reason and use trial and improvement

☆ Place the counters on the board below.

☆ Follow these rules. Try to swap the counters over, so that the red counters are where the yellows started and the yellows are where the reds started.

You need three red and three yellow counters.

Rules

You can move a counter into an empty square that is alongside it.

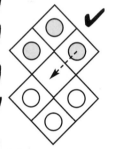

You can jump over another counter into an empty square, like this:

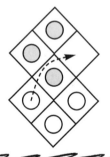

red

red   red

yellow   yellow

yellow

• **Count how many moves it takes. Do this several times.**

• **What is the fewest number of moves it takes you?** _____

Now try this!

• **What if there are two extra empty squares on the board?**

Talk to a partner about what you find out.

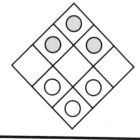

Teachers' note Ensure the children understand the rules of the task. Demonstrate the moves with the whole class at the start of the lesson. Encourage the children to count the number of moves, perhaps by marking a piece of scrap paper each time a counter is moved. Provide opportunities for the children to discuss what they did with a partner and, where possible, to show the way they moved the counters using the fewest moves.

Developing Numeracy
Using & Applying Maths
Year 3
© A & C BLACK